To: Dr.
Best

Pinkie Young

ONE CHILD'S
FAITH
ONE CHILD'S
COURAGE

A NOVEL

PINKIE YOUNG

Milligan Books

California

Copyright © 2004 by Pinkie Young
Los Angeles, California
All rights reserved
Printed and bound in the United States of America

Distributed by:
Milligan Books
1425 W. Manchester Blvd., Suite C
Los Angeles, California 90047
(323) 750-3592
(323) 750-2886 Fax

Book Formatting by Chris Ebuehi/Graphic Options
Los Angeles, CA

First Printing, April 2004
10 9 8 7 6 5 4 3 2 1

ISBN # 0-9753504-3-9

Publisher's note
This is a work of fiction. Names, characters, places, and
incidents either are products of the author's imagination or
are used fictitiously, and any resemblance to actual persons,
living or dead, events or locales is entirely coincidental.

All rights reserved. No part of this book may be repro-
duced in whole or in part, in any form or by any means,
electronic or mechanical, including photocopying, record-
ing or by any information storage and retrieval system,
without permission in writing from the author.

Dedication

This book is dedicated to all teenagers who feel alone, abandoned, hopeless or who are experiencing difficult times.

One Child's Faith, One Child's Courage is also dedicated to my natural and adopted children:

Eric,	Ja'Haan
Jason	Erinee
Princess	Roderick
Garmann	Nastassia
Tramel	Camille
Chanera	Eddie
Carl	Sade'
Craig	Nekayah

About the Author

Pinkie Young was born in the South, but came to California to visit and ended up staying. Although she enjoys urban life, she prefers rural living and dreams of moving back to the South someday. Naturally, her first novel, *One Child's Faith, One Child's Courage*, is about the South that she loves so much.

Pinkie Young is a Registered Nurse who earned a Bachelor of Science Degree from California State University, Long Beach and a Master's Degree from California State University, Los Angeles.

Pinkie Young currently resides in a rural Southern California area.

Acknowledgments

Grateful acknowledgment is due to Dr. Rosie Milligan and her associates for their assistance in helping me to realize a wonderful dream.

I thank God for all the individuals He placed in my life to encourage, inspire and guide me.

And of course, thanks to my family and all my friends, for always supporting me.

Chapter I

The First Awful Night

Wadley, Georgia

1940

One moonless December night, two sisters, Marie Green, age nine, and Patti Green, age six, were home alone, babysitting their baby brother, Jake, who was sleeping peacefully in the bedroom. The adults had gone out, leaving the oldest child Marie in charge.

A kerosene lamp, which cast its flickering shadow on the walls in an eerie monster shape, dimly lit the house.

"Ooh, my doll is prettier than yours," Marie said, holding up her paper doll she'd just cut out from newspaper.

"But mine is better dressed," Patti said. She had designed a dress and a big hat like the ladies at her church wore, to put on her paper doll. She was feeling nervous, but didn't want Marie to know she was afraid. Although she was the youngest, she often sensed things that even Marie didn't notice.

Patti had reason to be afraid. The family lived in the woods in a rear house. The front house was about one hundred feet away, closer to the road, so the family was very isolated. She needed to go to the outhouse to relieve herself, but she was afraid of the snakes which tended to come out at night. The wind blew through the surrounding pine trees. An owl hooted in the distance. The smell of pine filled the air. Patti trembled and her scissors shook, she was feeling such a sense of dread. What was wrong? She couldn't quite put her finger on it. The girls continued to play quietly with paper dolls in the front room of their three-room house, when, all of a sudden, they heard a loud knock at the front door.

Startled, the two girls looked up. "Who is it?" Marie asked timidly. Her voice cracked in fear.

Silence ensued. Marie called out again a little bit louder. Still, there was no response. Since there was no window in the house, they could not look out to see who it was. They stared at each other, not knowing what to do. Marie shrugged her shoulders and turned her palms upward to the ceiling. She seemed to be weighing it in her mind. Should she or shouldn't she open the door?

A wave of fear ran through Patti. She shuddered inside. Not knowing what to do, she froze. The adults had left instructions not to open the door. She wanted to tell Marie, "Don't open the door," but her tongue froze to the roof of her mouth.

After a minute, the girls heard a second knock.

"Who is it?" This time Marie spoke in

a loud, crisp voice. She seemed to hope if she sounded braver, whoever it was would go away. The latch on the door was not very strong. She pulled her index finger to her lip to hush her younger sister.

Patti's thoughts raced wildly. What if a murderer came in and killed all of the children?

Again no one answered.

The sisters looked at each other, eyes widened with fright. "Who's there?" Marie called nervously. Still no response. The seconds crept by slowly. Another moment passed. Then, they heard a third loud knock. The hairs on Marie's arm rose and she shivered. By then, fresh tears rolled down both sisters' faces. Who could be knocking this late at night?

Suddenly, a raspy male voice from

outside the house barked, "Marie, it's me. Let me in."

The girls tiptoed to the door. Patti's heart pounded so loudly, she had to lean on the door for support. Neither Marie nor Patti recognized the voice and both were afraid. They didn't have a telephone to call the sharecropper owner in the front house. The country was at war and even rations were considered a luxury. Most people in the country did not have telephones at this time.

"Open this door, Marie," the man demanded. Finally, Marie slowly eased the door open to determine who was knocking.

As soon as she opened the door, the muffled male voice demanded, "Marie, why did you open the door?" The voice grew threatening. "You are going to get a whipping for opening the door. We told you never to open the door when grown ups aren't home."

Initially, Marie and Patti couldn't see who was standing outside because not only was it pitch dark, there were no lights on the porch. All they could hear was this disembodied booming male voice. Was it a ghost?

Who could it be? Someone was hiding in the shadows. Marie had her hand on the latch, and slowly released it. The door flew open. At first, they saw no one. Finally, two adults moved closer to the doorjamb, until they stood in the square of light cast from the kerosene lamp in the front room.

Finally, Marie and Patti recognized who it was. It wasn't the boogie man. It was the girls' mom, Laura, and her new husband,

15

Mr. Willie, their stepfather. They stepped into the house. They had left the girls alone earlier in the day while they went out visiting. They had told the girls not to open the door and let strangers in.

Mr. Willie struck Marie with a belt that awful night. The mother stood and watched, but she didn't say anything or intervene. "Didn't I tell you not to open the door?" Mr. Willie said over and over with each lash. He didn't seem to consider the fact that he had demanded Marie to open the door.

When he turned to Patti, he said, "I'm gon' whip you too, for letting Marie open the door."

Patti started crying before the first lash landed on her legs. Out of the corner of her eyes, she watched her mother, who seemed to be just as afraid as her children. Even her four year old brother Jake woke up after hearing the commotion and began to cry.

"Shut up, boy, or I'll whup you, too," Mr. Willie called out to the bedroom. "This is my house and y'all gon' do what I say do."

Later that night, as she lay in bed with her sister and brother, Patti pondered her situation. Although her legs stung from the lashes, she felt more pain inside. Marie had cried herself to sleep, and Patti listened as Marie sniffled while she slept.

Confused, she wondered why had Mr. Willie frightened her and her sister? It seemed as if he had provoked and even set them up to open the front door that night. What if this had been serious? What if some stranger had been at the door and really harmed them? Hurt and angry, Patti didn't understand. Both girls were good children.

They helped with the housekeeping at home, received fairly good grades in school and babysat their younger brother.

Patti couldn't understand why they were tricked into opening the door, then whipped when they did. Why would an adult do this to a child? Was this poor judgment or abuse?

From that point on, Patti lost faith in the family to protect her and her sister. She never felt safe again at home.

After that awful night, Patti's childhood was often riveted with fear. She was afraid because time after time, she witnessed similar events. Oftentimes, Mr. Willie beat and frightened Marie, Patti and Jake, for no logical reason at all. Without saying it, Patti felt their stepfather not only didn't love them, he didn't like her and her sister and her brother. Was it because he was not their "real" father? Patti didn't know. Her mother and "real father" had separated when she was only two, so she didn't remember him.

All she knew was that this was a difficult and painful period in her life. She felt like this was a turning point—the beginning of what would become a "reign of terror" in their home life. Her mother had been remarried only two years at this time. Patti didn't mind her mother having a new husband. What bothered her was how Mr. Willie was beginning to change and act as though he did not care for them anymore. He'd treated Patti, Marie and Jake very warmly while he was courting their mother. After the marriage, he became distant, but he had not been abusive—that was, up until now. Patti didn't know what to do. She fell asleep, her mind in turmoil and dreamed of monsters chasing her all night.

Chapter II

Isolation

Naughtyville, Georgia

At that time, the Green children lived on a farm in a back house. The farm was not far from the small town of Wadley. The family worked as sharecroppers for a white family named Crocker. From sunup to sundown, they worked in the fields, growing fruits, vegetables and cotton. One-half of what they grew went to the landlord, Mr. Crocker, because he owned the land. This was their way of paying for the use of the land—as sharecroppers didn't pay rent. The family grew corn, watermelons, cantaloupes, sweet peas, cabbage, string beans, okra, onions, collard, mustard and turnip greens, sugar cane, sorghum as well as cotton. The landlord also received one-half of the profit from the cotton produced after it was sold.

The family lived on that small farm rent-free for two years after the mother's marriage to Mr. Willie. Right away, their mother, Laura, and Mr. Willie, had fraternal twins, a boy and a girl. Later, they moved to a more isolated area in Naughtyville, Georgia. Some people called this area, "The Backwoods."

There were only three houses in the new area which was surrounded by large towering oaks, cottonwoods, and elms. The three houses were approximately one-quarter mile apart. The family lived in the middle of the other two houses. There was no electricity, running water or gas in the house. Holes decorated the walls, ceilings and floors. Their mother used old newspaper to cover the holes in the walls and to stop the wind from whistling and cutting through the three rooms at night.

The roof was made of rusty tin and often leaked when it rained. The house only had three rooms and a front porch. The front room served as the living room, family room and adult bedroom. It had a fireplace that was used for heating the house and baking white potatoes, yams or sweet potatoes, and hot cakes. These were the family's main foods. This was the house they lived in when Mr. Willie began to beat the children and their mother on an ongoing basis.

The front room was located just behind the front porch and served as an entrance to the second room. The second room also had a back entrance that led to the backyard. This room had one bed for all the children to sleep. The mattress on the bed was stuffed with corn shucks. The pillows were filled with cotton and rags—this made them very soft. Sometimes there were ticks and bugs called cinches in the mattress, which bit the children.

On cold nights the children heated an

old smoothing iron in the fireplace. The iron was wrapped in a cloth and put in the bed to keep their feet warm. They slept under patchwork quilts and sheets made by their mother. Often, Patti felt cold and snuggled up to Marie for warmth. But it didn't help matters if Jake peed in the bed. Then the area of warmth would get cold as an icicle.

The quilts were made of old clothes and flour sacks. In those days flour sometimes came in a large cloth sack. The flour sacks were usually a floral print, and although they were made of burlap, they were pretty. Their mother made sheets, quilts and underwear for the girls and she often sewed their clothes from burlap.

The third and final room was the kitchen. It was also where the family took baths. It had an entrance off the front porch to the right of the front room. The kitchen had a black potbelly iron stove. It required wood for heating water and cooking. The children had to fetch sticks, wood and pine knots for the stove and fireplace in the nearby woods. Pine knots, which ignited quickly, were used to start the fire. Pine knots burned easily and ignited the sticks or wood.

Water for cooking and bathing was brought from nearby streams in buckets or pails. The family also had a well. The water was also used for washing clothes and drinking. The well water always had a fresh taste.

Patti and her siblings had to make numerous trips to the streams with small buckets to get water. In the winter, the water would freeze and have to be thawed out. The water was heated on the potbelly stove or in the fireplace. This had to be done before the children could wash their faces and eat breakfast.

The stove was also used for heating water for bathing. Baths were taken in the kitchen in a large galvanized tin tub. Usually baths were taken on Saturday night. There were holes in the kitchen walls.

While bathing, sometimes Patti observed Mr. Willie outside peeping through the holes in the kitchen walls. Patti became frightened because she also heard groaning noises. Patti knew who it was, but she didn't tell anyone. She was frightened and didn't want to upset her mother and sister.

The winters were harsh. The children had to walk practically everywhere they went, including school. Sometimes they got frostbite on their feet because of the holes in their shoes.

Breakfast for the children consisted mostly of cornbread, syrup and fatback or grease from the fatback. The hot grease from the fried fatback was used to heat the cold stiff syrup or molasses in the wintertime. It was poured over the syrup during the cold winter months.

Corn was taken to the mill in town to be ground or crushed into cornmeal. Cornmeal was used to make cornbread. Cornbread was made from cornmeal, eggs, milk, especially buttermilk, baking powder and salt. Cornbread was baked in the potbelly stove, in the fireplace, or on top of the stove. When it was cooked on top of the stove, it was made from cornmeal, salt and hot water. It was called "hot water" cornbread. Cornbread was also eaten with buttermilk.

The wooden milk churn sat in the corner of the kitchen. Buttermilk was made by churning regular cow's milk and removing the fat or butter. What was left was called buttermilk. The Green children had to milk the cows and churn the milk before they went to school.

In spite of the limited income, the family made the best of their resources. Although they had a dirt yard, the family planted flowers, such as zinnia, azaleas, and chrysanthemums. They had a levee and a pond where the family often fished when they wanted fried fish for breakfast, lunch or dinner.

The family had plenty of fruit during the summer as the property was surrounded by trees of all sorts: fig, lemon, peach, walnut, acorn, plum, pear, apple and pecan trees. There were blackberry bushes where the children picked the berries and their mother made cobblers and pies. Their mother made peach, apple, lemon, coconut and pecan pies. The family killed hogs, chickens, goats, ducks, opossums, coons, rabbits and other wild animals for food. The children picked pecans and sold them at the small town store.

Patti would always remember dew on the grass in the morning. When they went to the outhouse, they used newspaper and pages from catalogues for toilet tissue. Snakes, grasshoppers, worms, caterpillars, butterflies, and birds were seen through the hole in the ceiling of the outhouse. Birds would fly in formation overhead as they headed deeper South when the weather was cold.

The family made their own syrup from sugar cane and sorghum. They took the corn to a mill uptown to have the mill grind their corn, which made their cornmeal.

Sometimes Marie made homemade biscuits. Marie was an excellent cook especially for her age. She started cooking at age seven. She enjoyed learning to cook. Marie had an enormous responsibility because she was the oldest child. Marie cooked for the whole family.

Occasionally, when visitors came by on Sunday, they often praised Marie because of the excellent meals she prepared after church services. Sometimes the meals were served at home. Breakfast was eaten at home in the morning, lunch was taken to the field during harvesting, and dinner was served at home in the evening.

During the week lunch was taken to the fields where adults were busy growing fruits, vegetables and cotton. Fruits and vegetables were grown for food. Marie and Patti helped with the twins, worked in the fields, washed and ironed clothes, cleaned the house and kept the yard clean by sweeping it with tree branches. Both girls liked making everything look neat and clean. Marie often braided Patti's hair and kept it neat. Marie was obviously more intelligent and the driving force for the Green children. Patti was slow but eager to help her older sister whom she adored.

The children had a dog they called "Old George" and through him, they played many games. Like most children, they made up games, which broke up the monotony of the hard work of their childhood. They were very sad when "Old George" died.

However, Marie and Patti were very aware they were isolated from their mother's family. There were no maternal relatives nearby. The closest maternal relative was approximately eight to ten miles away. The only way to visit the family was to walk. Their mother Laura didn't have a job or money. Laura's father and brothers didn't visit. Her sisters seemed to be afraid to visit and complained about how Laura's husband was treating her and the three older children. The sister's husbands didn't visit either.

In spite of having food to eat, a roof over her head, and clothes on her back, albeit second-hand clothes, Patti never felt secure as a child. The children were not allowed to make noise, and they resented Mr. Willie and were glad when he was not home. They were able to laugh and play when he left home. Everyone was more talkative when he was absent.

Being afraid made Patti quiet and withdrawn as a young child. She became more of a loner. She often cried herself to sleep, worrying about her mother and siblings.

Chapter III

Close Calls

When Jake, the third child and oldest brother, was about six, he was often funny and mischievous, as many boys were. One day Jake was playing and clowning around. He was roughhousing through the house as he usually did, when suddenly things turned serious.

Mr. Willie was sitting in a wooden chair. For no apparent reason, he said, "I'm going to hang you, Jake." His voice sounded serious.

Jake stopped running around. Marie and Patti shuddered.

Mr. Willie stood up and placed a rope around Jake's neck. "Stand on this chair, boy!" Mr. Willie yelled.

Laura heard the commotion and rushed into the room. "What's wrong?" Laura asked in a frantic voice.

Mr. Willie used the chair to have Jake strung up from the rafters. Jake stood on the chair, trembling. "Don't hang me, Mr. Willie, please." He broke down in tears.

With the rope around his neck, he looked pitiful. He was flailing his arms and crying, "Please don't hang me, Mr. Willie."

Mr. Willie told Jake, "Make peace with your Maker because you are going to die."

Everyone looked on in horror. All Mr. Willie had to do was kick the chair leg and Jake's neck would have been broken.

The three children were shocked and terrified. They didn't know what Jake had done to deserve hanging. What was so bad that Jake should die? All they could remember was Jake playing as usual and running around.

Marie started screaming in bloodcurdling wails, she was so frightened. "Do something!" she begged her mother. She certainly didn't want her brother to be hung. The two sisters both began screaming, tears gushing down their faces.

Laura, looking frightened, stood frozen and helpless. Patti and Marie were used to Mr. Willie beating them and their brother. They were used to seeing their mother beaten as well. But this was different. Suddenly Laura screamed, "Stop and let him down!"

To believe their brother would be hung was unthinkable. Marie continued to plead with her mother to stop the torture and prevent the hanging. Laura and the children grabbed the chair screaming, "Stop! Stop! Don't hang him."

Finally, Mr. Willie released Jake from the noose. Although they continued to cry silently, the sisters were relieved. They never learned what Jake had done to be threatened with hanging.

From that day forth, Jake's playing was never the same again. Patti kept crying, sometimes silently inside. She remembered feeling this sadness throughout her childhood.

On another occasion, when Patti received a new outfit through the mail from her natural dad, she felt happy. However, it turned into a bittersweet event. Throughout her growing up years, her father sent clothes sometimes, but her mother would always be punished when they arrived. Patti did not understand why her poor, helpless, unemployed mother had to be beaten because her children received much needed clothing from their father.

On this last occasion, the three children were very brave. Mr. Willie came in the door with a post office package, looking angry, and asked Laura, "Did you ask him to send these?"

Laura looked frightened and timid. She finally spoke up. "No, I did not." But she took the package out of his hands.

In a quick motion, Mr. Willie snatched the package out of Laura's arms, then opened it. Patti, looking on, observed children's clothes. "You asked for these clothes, didn't you?" Mr. Willie said angrily. Without warning, Mr. Willie struck Laura with his fist. Laura fell back, holding her hand to her face.

Whenever the clothes arrived, a fight started. Laura was beaten even though she would not fight back. However, this time was different. Marie grabbed a broom and struck Mr. Willie on the head.

Patti ran outside and picked up a stick

from the yard. "Hit him hard," Marie told Patti. "Jake, use that iron rod on the porch!" Marie cried. All three children were crying, screaming and striking Mr. Willie. This time the three Green children in a concerted effort used sticks to defend their mother. The children hit Mr. Willie over and over with the sticks. After a few moments, Mr. Willie stopped fighting Laura.

"Oh, I can't believe this. The children jumped on me, and you didn't say anything," Mr. Willie said to Laura. Laura did not respond. She was crying and had bruises and scratches on her face.

This was the first time the three children had the courage to fight back as a team. Marie led the fight. This concerted defense proved to be a turning point in their lives.

Laura was no longer beaten when the

children were around. Moreover, the beatings decreased for the children as well. However, the verbal abuse and torture continued. "You are so stupid," Mr. Willie would tell the children. "You can't cook," he would tell Laura.

On a third occasion, Mr. Willie called Patti and Jake from outside to the front room. "Look for what you moved," he told the children.

The children didn't know what they had moved or misplaced. Baffled, they looked at each other. "What are we looking for? Jake asked Patti.

"I don't know," Patti replied.

"Get outside and look for it. I know y'all moved it," Mr. Willie told them.

They were sent marching around the outside and the inside of the house. They were never told what they were looking for. They continued looking, all the time not knowing what they were to find.

After several hours of marching like soldiers, and searching for heavens-knew-what, Mr. Willie came to the front door and said, "Stop looking."

The children never learned what they were looking for, even though apparently, whatever Mr. Willie wanted had been found. One thing for sure, they didn't have anything to do with its disappearance.

ooo

Patti recalled another time when she, Marie and Jake wanted to go to church one night. There was an annual revival at the church and the children were looking forward to going. The children asked their mother if they could go to the revival. Mr. Willie overheard the children asking Laura.

Mr. Willie interrupted. At first his voice tone was low. "No, you can't go." Then, he began to yell, "You can't go to revival, lying about getting religion."

When Mr. Willie left the house for a while, Marie begged her mother, "Mama, please let us go to revival."

Initially, Laura seemed reluctant to let the children go. Marie kept asking and finally Laura relented. "I don't care. Go ahead."

Marie was so glad that she gathered Patti and Jake and started running. It was several miles to the church and the children had to walk.

Later, when Mr. Willie returned home,

he was enraged to find that the children had disobeyed his orders and gone to church anyway.

As the children headed down the dirt road to revival, they heard Mr. Willie's voice in the distance bellowing, "Hey! Hey! Come back here!"

The children ran and hid in the woods from Mr. Willie. Marie picked up a stick to strike him but he didn't find them where they were hid in the thicket.

Finally, the children reached the church. They looked over their shoulders as they entered. Mr. Willie didn't follow them inside the church, even though he had come several miles to stop them from going to revival. He probably didn't want other church members to witness his actions.

When the children arrived home from

the revival about 10:30 p.m., it was pitch dark. Mr. Willie was sitting on the front porch, like Billy Goat Gruff, waiting for them. Jake was in front and walked by Mr. Willie first.

"Jake, where have you been?" Mr. Willie demanded.

Trembling, Jake kept walking and didn't respond. He just stumbled into the house.

Patti was the second child to walk by Mr. Willie. He asked her the same question. "Where have you been?"

Patti knew he followed them and saw them go into church. Patti didn't answer either, she was so scared.

Marie started to trudge past Mr. Willie. He asked, "Marie, where y'all been?"

Sick of his abuse, Marie felt a surge of courage. She answered sharply and forcefully, "We have been to church."

"Who told you to go to church?" he asked.

The children knew not to tell him their mother had given them permission to go to church. They were fearful Laura would receive a beating.

"Nobody told us to go to church!" Marie screamed.

Mr. Willie sucked in his breath as if the wind had been knocked out of him. He finally spoke up. "Go on in there and go to bed. I am going to whip your rumps in the morning!"

The children rushed to bed right away. They were fearful Laura was in danger. They listened but did not hear him hit their mother that night.

Fearing a beating, the children plotted

to kill Mr. Willie the next day.

"Let's kill Mr. Willie," Marie told Jake and Patti.

"Look, we can use the rope from the barn to tie him up," Patti replied.

Patti and Jake decided they would tie his arms and legs.

Marie said, "I'll put a rope around his neck."

They decided that the two younger children would put his head on a chopping block. Marie would use an axe to behead him. The children got the rope and the axe ready. They waited nervously all day for Mr. Willie to return home.

Fortunately, Mr. Willie left the house early in the morning, before the children awoke. He didn't return until late that evening. He didn't mention the whippings.

Although the children didn't feel completely safe, they didn't attempt to kill him. This elaborate plan was never executed.

As far as the Green children were concerned, their lives were already in shambles. What would have happened to them if they had murdered this adult? Would anyone even believe they were abused and mistreated?

They talked about the worst thing that would have happened to them if they killed Mr. Willie. Would they be sent away to some detention farm or returned home to their mother?

For the most part, the children were penniless and ragged. They only received clothes occasionally from their father as they were growing up. They often had holes in their shoes and socks. They wore hand-me-downs that their mother had sewed. Laura didn't have money or a job. In those days, the men were in charge of the finances, but there was not much money anyway.

There were no homeless or battered women's shelters at the time so there was no place to go.

Patti felt helpless and trapped. She didn't feel protected. They were in a quagmire of despair. She always offered to help Laura but what could she do? After all, she was only a child.

Why did Mr. Willie treat them so cruelly? Patti questioned. Was mental illness a factor in all this rage and mis-treatment or was he demon possessed? It was too horrible for Patti to imagine.

○○○

Patti remembered a troubling incident that concerned her. It was a day when Marie had cooked and served everyone before she fixed her own plate to eat. A lot of responsibility fell on Marie's shoulders to cook and to help care for the younger children. Marie's cooking was very good. Laura was a good cook also. Patti could cook, but her cooking skills did not measure up to Marie's or Laura's. As they said, "Patti's cooking was a third distant cousin to her mother's and big sister's."

Everyone had been served. Marie finally started to eat her own food. One of the twins started to cry for Marie's food even though he had finished eating his own. There was no other food left. Marie was ordered by Mr. Willie to, "Give the boy that food."

"I haven't eaten and there is none left," Marie replied.

"Give the boy that food," Mr. Willie threatened.

It must have been horrible to have cooked for the whole family, served everyone, and then be ordered to give your food to someone who had already eaten.

Generally Marie was compliant, but this day, she'd had enough. "I won't do it," Marie answered. Marie took the plate and threw it on the table, spilling half of the food. There was nothing else for her to eat. It was sad to be hungry, Patti felt.

Chapter IV

Good Neighbors, Bad Neighbors

After the twins were born, Marie and Patti began to notice that their mother was losing weight. When Laura first married Mr. Willie, she had been a very attractive, caramel-colored woman. Her thick hair hung below her shoulders.

After a few years of marriage, Laura became thin, even though she had been a full-figured woman. She lost her teeth. She walked around mumbling to herself. She wore a head rag around her head to stop what she called "severe headaches."

However, Laura had no one to turn to. She was proud and didn't have friends or family near the farm where they lived.

"How do you feel, Mama?" Patti asked.

"I feel tired," Laura told Patti. "My head hurts."

There was no maternal extended family within eight to ten miles to help. Family members were distrustful and fearful of getting involved. Wives belonged to their husbands. People did not believe in interfering in marital affairs.

Only the husband's family members lived nearby. They usually treated Laura very poorly. Sometimes they didn't speak to the family. They walked by the house without coming in or speaking. Patti felt they were angry because her mother had three children, and this was a second marriage for both parties. The children didn't understand.

One day one of Laura's sisters-in-law walked by with her head covered. She didn't speak or come in.

Patti heard her mother mumble, "I know I didn't do anything to them."

On occasions, Patti noticed that Sally, the sister-in-law, sometimes had bruises as well.

Patti cried. Why was her mother being

treated so unfairly? Where was God? Didn't He know what was happening to her mother? Didn't He see what was happening?

Why had Mr. Willie beaten her mother and accused her of being romantically involved with his older brother Peter? Didn't he know this was her brother-in-law? This man had his own family and seemed to treat his wife well. Patti's mother, was quiet, patient and kind. Why was she treated like a caged animal?

○○○

There was a kind couple who lived several miles away. They were named Mr. and Mrs. Homer. Without saying a word, they seemed to understand the situation

Laura and her three older children were in. They brought apples and oranges to the children for Christmas. Usually, that was all the children received.

Mr. Ray Homer was the family patriarch of three generations. He was also the children's Sunday school teacher. He would stop by on Sunday and drive the children to Sunday school. This was the only positive thing Patti saw in her young life other than her mother's love. The Homer family demonstrated cohesiveness and caring.

"Why can't my family be like that?" Patti wondered.

The Homers were a God-fearing family. The couple were happily married and had several children. The children were sent to the best schools and took piano lessons. Patti stayed in touch with the family for years. The Homers' spirit and generosity stayed etched in Patti's mind. Through abuse, abandonment, hurt and pain, Patti always remembered how kind and unselfish Mr. Homer was.

It gave Patti confidence, strength, and trust in God. This reassurance in someone's goodness caused her faith to get stronger and allowed her to move forward. They were the best friends Patti had known in her young life. The Homers demonstrated their awareness of the Greens' plight through their kindness, but they never asked questions or passed judgment. They only tried to help the family.

Chapter V

Bad News and Good-Bye

When Patti was about ten years old, Marie gave her some devastating news. Something strange happened to Marie while their mom was at church one night.

Marie had been told not to discuss the situation, but thank God she told Patti.

"While you were asleep and mother was at church, Mr. Willie took me out of the bed and took me to the front room. He removed my underclothes and told me not to tell anyone."

Pattie turned pale and sat back down on the bed. Had Marie been touched inappropriately? Patti shivered. Both girls cried as they held each other, but neither told their mother.

Patti was already nervous and frightened because of past physical abuses. This added more stress during her young life. Patti started to blame her natural father for their plight.

She wondered if he cared. Did he know how his children were being treated? There was no phone to call him. Why did he let them live in such a condition? Didn't he care? It was not until Patti was a grandmother that she learned her father had to be prevented from using his gun to protect her when she was a child and being abused.

After learning of Marie's terrible night, Patti was always on guard. Early one morning the children were taken to an isolated field away from the house. Mr. Willie told Jake, "Go home and get lunch."

Then he turned to Patti. "Go to the neighbor's farm and fetch that hoe I left over there."

The farm was about a mile away. Patti was suspicious. She imagined what was going to happen to her sister, Marie. Patti was frightened. Her fear drove her to run all the way to the neighbor's farm and back to the field. As Patti was approaching the isolated field, she observed Marie running toward her. Marie had scratches on her face and neck. Patti assumed what had happened but she didn't know.

"What happened?" Patti asked Marie. Marie didn't answer. She kept running toward home.

Patti felt she had done the right thing to run instead of walk. Both girls ran home which was about three to four miles away.

Marie explained to their mother what had happened in the field. Laura was devastated. She sent for her mother-in-law, Faye. Faye stated the girls were making things up and not telling the truth. She supported her son who was at least forty years old. She further accused Laura of not being intimate with her husband, if the girls were telling the truth. How could Laura not be intimate when she was pregnant at the time and had small children? Laura told Faye she had been intimate with her husband. She also told Faye that her husband had accused her of being intimate with his brother.

Thank God, Marie had been able to speak up. Patti shuddered to think what might have happened had her sister not divulged the truth. So many young girls are not so brave.

Word spread quickly throughout the town about how Marie was treated. Patti was hurt. She was ashamed and embarrassed. She felt the family was the "laughing stock" in the whole region.

As for Laura, her hands and feet were tied. She didn't have a job or money. She had small children. What a tragedy! There was no shelter for battered women. Men were not subjected to jail time for abusing their wives and children. There was nowhere to go to be safe with five young children.

Laura had a sister named Ella. Ella was visiting her other sister Barbara at least one hundred twenty miles away when she heard the awful news about Marie. Ella called the Sheriff and explained what had happened to Marie. One day Patti was standing on the front porch when she saw the Sheriff drive up. Laura, her husband and Marie saw the Sheriff also.

Laura's husband quickly instructed her to have Marie deny what had happened in the field. He hid his head in a corner so the Sheriff wouldn't see him tell Marie to deny the incident.

"Tell her to say nothing happened," Mr. Willie told Laura. Laura didn't respond.

Patti vividly recalled the incident as though it happened yesterday. There were two officers in a vehicle. When the officers approached, they asked, "What happened out here?"

"Nothing," Mr. Willie replied.

"Who is Marie?" one officer asked.

"I'm Marie." Marie stepped forward.

"Did something happen to you?" Sheriff Jones asked Marie.

Marie had been instructed to deny everything and she did. The Sheriff accepted what Marie said and left after a few minutes.

Marie dropped her head. They didn't take Marie aside and ask her what happened. They didn't examine Marie or take her to a doctor. If they had looked closer, they would have seen the scratches on her face and neck. They just walked away.

Luckily, Aunt Ella was persistent, even though she was visiting her sister Barbara. Aunt Ella sent someone else to come and remove Marie from the farm. A man and lady came by and asked, "Marie, would you like to live with us?"

"Yes," Marie told them.

The couple were Mr. and Mrs. Aaron Daily. The Dailys were longtime family friends. "You will be able to live with us and go to school with our daughter. Would you enjoy that?" they asked Marie. Marie was eager to go.

"I want to go also," Patti said sadly.

"Maybe you can go next time," Mrs.

Daily said. Patti wanted to go but she couldn't. She loved Marie so much. Marie was her role model and she often imitated her. If Marie didn't wear lipstick, Patti wouldn't wear lipstick. If Marie learned to curl her hair, Patti wanted to curl her hair also.

Patti asked Laura, "Why can't I go, Mama?"

"I need your help," Laura told her. Patti was sad because her best friend who was also her sister was gone. Patti was happy for Marie, but it was a sad good-bye. She didn't get to see Marie for several years.

Marie seemed eager to go with the Dailys, but sad to be away from Laura and the younger children. After she left, Marie wrote to Laura and Patti frequently.

"Marie writes really well," Laura told

Patti. Patti was happy to receive Marie's letters. Reading the letters was like reading a short novel.

Marie was smarter and much stronger than Patti. The Dailys were a wonderful couple and Marie felt safe, protected and secure. They lived in a larger Georgia town. She wrote about her new experiences but it was much different from being with her family. Marie was thoughtful, witty and nurturing. She enjoyed cooking for the family, but she missed playing with Jake and Patti after completing their work.

"I am studying hard so that I can go to college. I want to go to law school," Marie wrote.

Chapter VI

Patti's Nightmare

Spring

Patti experienced more fear and trauma after Marie left. Just as the field was blossoming with shiny new spring plants, Patti was beginning to blossom into adolescence. When she was twelve, Mr. Willie took Patti and Jake to the same isolated field. Patti was afraid because she felt she knew what was going to happen. She was right. Patti had given much thought to this day.

Just as Patti expected, Mr. Willie instructed Jake, "Go to the Smiths' farm. I left my tools over there."

This time the farm was farther away and in a different direction. It was much farther than Patti was asked to travel when Marie was left behind. But Patti was ready.

As soon as Jake was out of sight, Mr. Willie unzipped his trousers and exposed himself. He asked Patti, "Do you want to see something?"

Patti angrily replied in a forceful voice, "No, I don't want to see anything. And if you bother me, I'll tell my grandpa!"

Mr. Willie quickly zipped his trousers. There was no other conversation. Patti and Mr. Willie fell silent. They continued to work in the field. When Jake returned he didn't know what had happened and Patti didn't tell him. Patti didn't want to hurt her mother again. She didn't tell her mother until she was thirty-seven years old.

When they finished working in the fields that day, they rode their horses home. Jake and Patti rode the same horse. Jake sat in front and Patti was behind him. Patti heard very disturbing sounds that infuriated her. They were the same sounds she heard when she was in the bathtub taking baths.

When Patti heard the sounds, she wondered what had happened to Mr. Willie's older daughter from his first marriage. She wondered if the first wife was abused also. There had been rumors about an attempted poisoning of the first wife. She had heard that he had locked his first wife in the barn. Had there really been an attempted poisoning? Would her mother be next?

Would Patti and Jake be included also? Was this nightmare true? Patti was afraid but she didn't want to destroy her mother with the news of what happened in the field that day. It had been a horrible experience. She couldn't fathom hurting her mother. She didn't tell Laura until much later in life. Laura looked shocked and sad after hearing the news.

After that horrible experience in the field, Patti later learned the family was moving again. This time it was to an even more isolated area. This time there were no other houses around. What was going to happen to her, Laura and Jake? At this time, no maternal family members were coming to visit them. Patti suspected they were angry or afraid. Evil is so powerful and can inflict fear in people.

The new area where they moved was about a mile from the railroad tracks. There were no other houses or people around. Marie was gone. Patti felt alone. It was a pleasure just to see the train pass by even though that was only a few times a month.

Patti and Jake walked several miles to school each day. School was held in the same building where church was held on Sundays. School was the only outside contact they had with other people. Patti and Jake tried to go to Sunday school but were not always permitted. Patti had a reason to be fearful about the latest move.

ooo

One cold morning when she was thirteen, she heard a raspy, chilly voice say to her and Jake, "Y'all go and live with your people."

Patti was shocked. Laura stood nearby. She was pregnant again. Laura seemed stunned. She had no money or a job. She objected to her children being sent away. "If they leave, I am leaving also."

She was not permitted to go, but Patti and Jake were forced to leave.

As the two children packed their clothes, Patti had a sick feeling in her stomach. She wanted to leave the area, but she didn't want to leave her mother behind. She wanted to cry, but she wouldn't because she refused to worry her mother.

"We will be okay, Mama," Patti reassured her mother. Patti's mother didn't know where Patti and Jake were going.

As they walked away from the house, Patti asked Jake, "Where are you going?"

"I am going to Grandpa Fred's house. Where are you going?"

"I am going to Aunt Ella's house."

Grandpa Fred lived thirteen miles from Aunt Ella.

"Be strong," Patti told Jake as she headed toward Aunt Ella's house and her brother proceeded toward Grandpa Fred's house. She loved Jake so much and didn't want him to go.

From years of hard work, both children

were very strong for their age. Patti was thirteen and Jake was eleven. Patti had one pair of shoes but they were too small and caused corns on her feet. She wore the shoes because it was cold outside. She didn't have deodorant and recalled smelling her own body odor after walking to her aunt's house. Patti didn't get to see Jake because of the distance between her grandfather's and aunt's houses.

When she arrived at Aunt Ella's home, Patti was afraid and ashamed to tell her aunt what had happened. Jake was not afraid to tell their grandfather. Jake was stronger. He explained what happened. The grandfather didn't go to get Laura and the rest of the children. Why didn't someone call the Sheriff to go get her mom? Maybe Aunt Ella did call, Patti later thought.

Afterwards, Patti didn't get to see Jake often. Grandpa Fred was elderly and didn't have a car. Aunt Ella didn't have a car either. There were no busses or taxi cabs. The Greyhound bus did not travel in that part of the country.

Few people owned automobiles. Some people would charge a fee to transport residents to the Greyhound bus station or hospital fifty miles away. Patti felt she had lost her sister and best friend Marie. Now she was losing her mother and brother Jake. This was very painful and almost too much for Patti to bear. Patti prayed nightly for her mother and siblings. This gave her strength. Aunt Ella loved Patti and encouraged her. But there was no true substitute for her mother's love. Patti loved her mother and siblings so much.

ooo

Word spread throughout the area about the two children being forced in the street. No one helped or interfered. No one offered food, money or to help the family. Were they that afraid? The church didn't offer assistance either. Patti was sad because she didn't get to see or visit her brother Jake or her mother or her younger siblings.

Patti had to walk several miles alone back to her old school in order to graduate. She had to walk past the old road where her mother and the other children were. Her mother was several miles off the road in the isolated area.

Patti cried as she walked past the dirt road leading to where her pregnant mom was. Patti was ashamed because her shoes were too small and she could smell her own body odor when she arrived at school. She cried silently but never explained why Jake was absent.

Patti loved school. She wanted to be smart like her older sister Marie, who was sent away several years earlier. Each day as she walked, Patti reveled in looking at God's beautiful creation along the country road. The fields were filled with an array of beautiful wild flowers of all colors—azure sky blue, cornflower yellow, royal and violet purple. Yes, she knew there was a God. After walking about five to six miles to and from school each day, Patti finally graduated from middle school.

ooo

Graduation was a big event for Patti. Her parents had only completed the fourth or fifth grade. Her teachers were usually not college graduates.

Patti was the only student graduating in her class that year. It was a fairly small school.

Naturally, Patti wanted her parents to attend the ceremony. Patti watched and waited for her mom to walk through the door.

Patti wanted her mom to see the white dress her dad had bought for her graduation. The white dress was trimmed in gold. The dress looked Japanese in style. Her mother never came to the ceremony. Patti cried and was very hurt. She feared for her mother's safety. Patti later learned her mother was not permitted to come to the ceremony as she was nine months pregnant and would have had to walk miles to the middle school to see Patti graduate.

Chapter VII

A Joyful Time

Marie came back to visit when her mother had the baby. She stayed with Aunt Ella and Patti. Fearing for their safety, Aunt Ella didn't want Patti and

Marie to go visit their mother. She was afraid for the girls because their mother was still in the isolated area with no other people around. Patti was hurt and became selectively mute.

Patti wrote to another aunt, Barbara, and asked if she could come and live with her to go to high school. Aunt Barbara never responded. Marie became vocal and refused to obey Aunt Ella when she told the girls they couldn't visit their mother Laura.

"You must be crazy," Marie protested.

The two sisters walked five to six miles to see their mother and the new baby. They were happy to hold the new arrival before returning to Aunt Ella's house.

Both girls got a job earning $2.50 a week to help out. Marie left again to live with the Dailys, and Patti was very sad.

She hated to see her sister leave. She couldn't see her brother Jake either. She cried more and more and became more selectively mute. Aunt Ella was very encouraging because Patti was very obedient. They developed a bond that lasted for life.

Even though Aunt Barbara didn't respond to the letter to let Patti come and go to school, another door opened for her. Aunt Barbara was closer, more than one hundred miles away, but it was Aunt Lillie who came to get Patti.

Aunt Lillie had a daughter named Madeline. Madeline told Patti, "Please come live with us and walk to school with me. You will like where I live. We can come to get you in a car."

Patti found out that Madeline wanted a sister and had been asking her mom to let someone live with them. Madeline wanted someone to walk her to school. Aunt Lillie decided to take Patti to live with her and Madeline.

Patti traveled more than three thousand miles from Georgia to Oregon by automobile to live with Aunt Lillie and Madeline. Patti was so happy. She worked hard and tried to be obedient. She studied hard. Patti cleaned the house, cut the grass, and washed and ironed the clothes. Patti also attended school while doing odd jobs such as baby-sitting and cleaning houses and trailers. Patti earned $8 a week. She contributed $5 to the household and used the other $3 for the beauty shop, lunch, bus fare. She also bought her school clothes.

When Patti graduated from high school, she was able to purchase her own class ring, sweater, skirt, yearbook and medallion. Patti did not get a chance to go to the prom. She didn't have the money to purchase a prom dress but she was on the honor roll at school. She worked babysitting, on the night of the prom. Patti didn't care. She had graduated from high school.

Patti graduated from high school on a Friday, and she was blessed to obtain a job the Monday after graduation. Patti worked days and attended college at night. College classes ended at 9:50 p.m. Patti rode two buses approximately fifteen miles and walked another five blocks to Aunt Lillie's house after classes. Patti read the Bible and prayed every night before she went to bed. She also cried every night about her mother and younger siblings. Patti set the clock to get up at 5:30. She had to ride three buses to get to work by 8:00. Patti developed a habit of not being late or absent from college or work.

Lillie had given Patti an opportunity to have a better life and help her mother. Patti didn't want to disappoint her mother or Aunts Ella and Lillie. As Patti was away from her mother and siblings for many years, she didn't receive phone calls from either of her parents during that time. The siblings were younger and didn't have the means to call. After Patti started working, she went to a phone booth and called her mom.

Patti cried and prayed daily about her mother and siblings as well as the enormous responsibility her mother had. Patti sent money to help her mother with the children.

She and her mom corresponded mostly by mail. Her mother didn't have money to pay for phone calls and she had no telephone.

Chapter VIII

Mr. Willie

Patti hadn't seen Mr. Willie for many years. One day, when she was twenty-two, while on vacation in Georgia, she decided to spend a night with Aunt Ella.

Patti hoped to see just one classmate or the teacher she knew nine years earlier. She started to walk to a store in the small town. Suddenly, a truck passed by carrying several men.

"Hey," Patti heard a voice yell. She didn't stop walking.

"Hey there, you," the voice yelled again. Without warning the truck stopped. Patti looked back, her heart beating wildly. One man exited the truck and began running toward Patti. Not knowing what to expect, Patti quickened her step and didn't look back anymore.

"Patti, you know you hear me," the man said.

Patti stopped and looked more closely. The man was no longer as tall and foreboding as he'd been when she was a child.

"Do you know who I am?" the man asked after catching up to Patti.

Patti was shocked and startled. "Yes, I know who you are," she answered in an angry tone.

"Who am I?" he asked, smiling as though he expected a warm response from Patti.

"You are Willie Clark!" she acknowledged in a frightened voice. Her heart began pounding loudly, and she felt her hands tremble.

"Where you goin'?" questioned Mr. Willie.

"None of your business," Patti said, rushing away. Patti wanted Mr. Willie to know that she didn't wish to communicate in any way.

When Patti returned to Aunt Ella's house, she told her about the encounter. Aunt Ella threatened to contact the Sheriff if Mr. Willie attempted to talk to Patti again. Ella really loved her niece Patti.

ooo

Patti didn't see Mr. Willie again for another twenty years. When she saw him again, it was indirectly because of her mother.

Over the years, Laura had always been prayerful and read the Bible. Praying gave Laura solace and strength. Patti felt Laura was able to do as the Bible says, "love ye your enemies, and do good." Patti was not as empathetic as Laura.

At the time Mr. Willie developed a serious heart condition, he asked Laura to take care of him. Laura had such a for-giving spirit that she nursed Mr. Willie and led him to Christ before his demise. Patti had ambivalent feelings about her mother's sympathetic, compassionate and benevolent duty, but she refused to express her concerns, fearing she would burden her mom.

Each day Mr. Willie grew weaker and was unable to perform any self-care activities such as feeding or bathing himself. Consequently, Laura washed and pressed his clothes and helped him dress each morning. In addition, Mr. Willie had to be dressed for bed each night. Laura bathed Mr. Willie and combed his hair. She made sure that Mr. Willie kept his doctor's appointments, obtained medications from the pharmacy, completed laboratory test, and took the medications prescribed. In order to follow the doctor's instructions,

Laura had to cook special foods and feed him three times a day.

At this time, Laura was a senior citizen herself. Patti grew very concerned about her mother's declining health. To compound matters, the stress of caring for an elderly person was taking its toll on Laura.

"How are you holding up, Mother?" Patti questioned Laura. "You look so tired!"

"I am doing the best I can," Laura answered sadly.

Patti knew that through the years, Laura had helped her elderly neighbors. She had washed and pressed the neighbors' hair, mended their clothes, shopped for food and even bathed them.

All her life, Laura had been a very strong woman, emotionally and physically, but this was different. Nursing Mr. Willie was a twenty-four-hour effort. Laura didn't get much rest because of this full-time activity. Patti wanted desperately to intervene but kept her composure. She loved Laura so much.

Chapter IX

The Escape

Later in life, Patti asked her mother, "How did you escape from the isolated situation you were left in when Jake and I were forced to leave?"

Laura pondered this question for a moment. Then she said, "I prayed." Laura told Patti that she prayed for a specific date to escape or be released. Laura said she prayed to leave by March fourth of that year. There was no phone to communicate with anyone. There were no other houses or people around.

"However, one day a total stranger stopped by. I didn't know the person. I was sure of my eventual escape so I gave this stranger a note to take to my oldest sister, Abby. The note asked Abby to send someone to help me escape."

Laura had prepacked her suitcase and sewing machine. She continued her story. "I gave the stranger the sewing machine along with the note to take to Abby. I hid the prepacked suitcase under the bed. I saw voodoo dust under the bed on my side. I moved the voodoo dust to the other side of the bed and this was when I was able to escape."

After Abby received the note from Laura, she sent someone to get her younger sister. Abby was not afraid. She knew the situation Laura was in because she had stayed with her during the birth of the twins. She didn't visit Laura any more because there were conflicts with Mr. Willie about where she would sleep. Abby was much more vocal and courageous than Laura.

Laura told Patti that on March third of that year, "I looked at the gate outside, which was about three hundred feet from the house. There was a man standing at the gate near a car."

Laura said, "I knew God had answered

my prayers. I grabbed my two youngest children and the packed suitcase and ran for my life. The twins were left behind because I knew I would never be permitted to take all the children without a fight and I had no money or job." Laura added, "I felt I would be better able to get them after I escaped." She was mistaken.

Initially, Laura went to Abby's house. Mr. Willie tracked her down. He tried to get her to leave Abby's house. Abby was strong and refused to let Mr. Willie come on her property. Rumors spread. Word was that Mr. Willie stood about one hundred feet from Abby's house preaching and repeating, "What God has put together let no man put asunder."

Laura had to escape again. This time she went to Abby's daughter's house. Her husband located her again and took the oldest of the two children that Laura had escaped with. Laura still had no job. She had to find one quickly so that she could fight to get her children back.

At the time of Laura's escape, when Patti learned about her mother's dilemma, she became stressed. Prayer was the only answer for this situation. Patti was three thousand miles away and had no way to help her mother because she was in high school. She had no funds to travel home to help her mother.

Finally, Laura found a job as a maid at a small hotel. Laura asked her oldest daughter, Marie, to move back home and help her. Marie gladly obliged. Laura and Marie both worked at the same hotel. Later they rented a room together.

Laura finally went to court to fight for her children. The court awarded Laura three of the children. One of the twins was awarded to Mr. Willie. The sheriff was contacted to help her pick up the children. Laura received a better job with benefits. She saved money and purchased a home for her and her children. Again, Laura said she felt the Lord had answered her prayers and demonstrated His power.

Laura later told Patti, "I prayed and asked God to never let my children be in the streets begging for bread."

Laura's prayers for her children were answered, too. Although she had wanted to become an attorney, Marie dropped out of school, delaying her education. Instead, as an obedient daughter, Marie, helped Laura finish bringing up the younger set of children. Later, Marie married and raised twin girls. She returned to college and obtained a degree when her daughters were teenagers.

Jake graduated from high school and got married. He was a devoted husband and father. He attended a trade school and became a welder helping to build ships.

Gary, the twin who wanted to remain behind to help his father, Mr. Willie on the farm, enlisted in the military and made a career of it.

Chapter X

Forgiveness

Even though she was young, Patti understood her mother's situation. She decided early in life that she didn't want to be homeless again. Patti didn't want her children to suffer as she had as a child. Patti decided to work hard and finish school. She also decided to go to college. Her Aunt Ella had instilled in her the need to succeed and obtain a college education.

She didn't give Patti an option. Aunt Ella was very caring and had taught Patti to be a good housekeeper and homemaker.

"I don't intend to let you sit around and not make some thing of yourself," Aunt Ella informed Patti when she first moved in with her. She championed and facilitated every move to ensure Patti graduated middle school with honors.

"You must do well all through school in order to get into college. You may be the first one in the family to graduate from college. I will always be there for you," Aunt Ella assured Patti. Patti accepted Aunt

Ella's challenge and graduated with honors from middle school, high school and college.

When Patti was graduating from college, she called her mother and told her how hurt, disappointed and even embarrassed she was when her mom was not present at the past graduation ceremonies. Laura apologized to Patti, "I am sorry. But I want to come to your college graduation."

Patti sent her mother an airplane ticket to attend the ceremony. Laura consented and finally came to see her daughter graduate for the first time. Laura was so pleased and proud when Patti received an "Outstanding Student" Award.

Patti was surprised also. Laura witnessed the graduation and Patti felt another prayer had been answered. Not only had her mom come to the ceremony, there were guests from several states. Patti's friend Connie came from the east coast. Patti's paternal Aunt Lois traveled four hundred miles to see her graduate. Patti was the first one in the family to obtain a college education. Her mom and her aunts were proud of her.

Aunt Lois was a God-fearing, praying woman. Although Patti had a difficult time while she was young, she could really communicate with Aunt Lois. Aunt Lois always had an encouraging word for Patti. She gave Patti the strength needed to endure difficult times.

Patti was able to contact Aunt Lois when she was lonely, hurt or in trouble. Patti didn't see or hear her parents or siblings' voices for almost a decade until she started earning enough money to call her mom or travel to Georgia.

When she learned she could be close to Aunt Lois, it helped her. Patti could relate to Aunt Lois. Aunt Lois would pray with Patti and tell her "you can make it." Patti could always rely on encouragement from Aunt Lois. "The only problem you have had was hard times," Aunt Lois would tell Patti. Patti remained very close to Aunt Lois for more than thirty years.

They spoke on the phone weekly and visited each other frequently. They read the Bible and prayed together. Patti obeyed her favorite paternal aunt. It was a sad day when Aunt Lois expired. Patti lost an aunt, friend, prayer partner and mentor.

Patti did "make it," as Aunts Lois, Lillie and Ella predicted. She was a hard worker. She was promoted to the second highest position in her department in banking. As an adult, she volunteered and worked with many children. She also inspired many children to go to college.

Over the years, Patti became very close to Aunt Lois's son Ron. Aunt Lois was proud of their close relationship. She encouraged it. Aunt Lois felt they were "able to really talk and get along." Aunt Lois prayed for the whole family and stressed the importance of family relationships. Patti and Ron visited each other. Patti, Ron, and his wife Betty often traveled together. They became like sisters and brothers.

Patti loved life and needed close friends. Her sisters and brothers didn't communicate often. Being separated geographically from the family, Patti developed strong attachments to close friends. She was not jealous or unforgiving which endeared her to many people. Most of the time she accepted her friends as they were. Although Patti had a quiet temperament, she was loyal to her friends and family. People who got to know her found her to be dependable and considerate. In spite of her shyness, she learned to be assertive, yet congenial.

During many situations in her life, Patti had to remember the Biblical scripture that states, "For if ye forgive men their trespasses, your heavenly Father will also forgive you: But if ye forgive not men their trespasses, neither will your Father forgive your trespasses."

∘∘∘

Patti was a private person, who didn't care for gossiping. Neither did she disclose her personal life story to many people. One day Patti opened up and told a close friend about her childhood.

The friend broke down and cried. When she pulled herself together, she commented, "I have never heard you speak negatively about your mother and father. Were you angry with them?"

Surprisingly, Patti smiled at her friend. She paused before she spoke. "Once another friend asked me the same question. He was a counselor and wanted to know if I was angry or felt abandoned. I told him I could honestly say I did not. I knew my mother had done all she could and my dad did not witness what happened."

○○○

However, Patti was angry with Mr. Willie not only for the abuse, but for separating her from the family. Even so, Patti was determined not to be consumed by the past.

One Saturday morning, years later, Patti was sitting in the audience at a hotel where a women's conference was being held. The visiting guest speaker said, "You must forgive all those who have hurt you whether they are living or dead." Mr. Willie was deceased.

"God, please help me to forgive Mr. Willie today," Patti prayed and cried. That was the day Patti forgave Mr. Willie. She felt as though a burden had been lifted from her shoulders. Finally Patti was free from anger. Now she was able to teach young people about forgiveness.

Although Patti had missed her parents as a young child, she was able to call and visit them when she was an adult. She reconciled with her biological father at age 40. She was able to enjoy both parents and visit them until she was a senior citizen. When both elderly parents became ill, she was able to move in and help provide care for them until they died.

Looking back, Patti never forgot the trials she experienced as a child, but she was able to release them and lead a productive, fulfilling life. She learned that people do not have to remain victimized by their pasts, and that with enough courage, you can reshape your life.

Not only did Patti learn survival skills

growing up, she learned the lesson of faith. She learned it was possible to succeed against the odds when you had faith. She also learned this important lesson—that good will always triumph and love will prevail. It wasn't what happened to you in life, but how you reacted to what happened to you. She learned to turn tragedy into victory.

BOOK AVAILABLE THROUGH

Milligan Books, Inc.

One Child's Faith, One Child's Courage $12.00

Order Form

Milligan Books, Inc.

1425 W. Manchester Ave., Suite C, Los Angeles, CA 90047

(323) 750-3592

Name_____ Date _____

Address_____

City_____ State____ Zip Code _____

Day Telephone _____

Evening Telephone_____

Book Title_____

Number of books ordered___ Total ....$ _____

Sales Taxes (CA Add 8.25%) ....$ _____

Shipping & Handling $4.90 for one book ..$ _____

Add $1.00 for each additional book..........$ _____

Total Amount Due....................................$ _____

    Check   Money Order   Other Cards _____

    Visa   MasterCard Expiration Date _____

Credit Card No. _____

Driver License No. _____

    Make check payable to Milligan Books, Inc.

Signature   Date